GLACIER
NATIONAL PARK
Journal

Journal Collections

America's National Parks Series
GLACIER NATIONAL PARK

Book Number 4
Wildflowers and the Garden Wall

HUZZAH PUBLISHING
P.O.Box 684, Columbia Falls, MT 59912

ISBN 978-0-9989352-0-1

First Edition March 2019

PRINTED IN THE UNITED STATES OF AMERICA

Design by Miantae Metcalf McConnell
Cover Photograph: Don Geyer

www.huzzahpublishing.com

You will notice that this journal contains lined pages and blank pages. After each set of six lined pages come two blank pages. Blank pages provide opportunities to sketch, doodle, or write some more, as you see fit.

My GLACIER NATIONAL PARK *Journal*

Beginning Date_____

Ending Date_____

Thank You

for choosing

GLACIER NATIONAL PARK JOURNAL

America's National Park Series

If you enjoyed the cover art and
quality of this product, please give us a
thumbs up review on Amazon, Barnes
& Noble, or other bookseller websites.

We sincerely thank you for your
patronage and are proud to have
provided a vessel for your expression.

www.huzzahpublishing.com

Huzzah Publishing offers several lines of journals.
We are known for our signature photographs.

If you would like to purchase another journal,
please check with your retail or online bookstore.

**see next page for additional
Glacier National Park Journals**

3 more Glacier National Park journals

GRINNELL LAKE

AURORA BOREALIS

COLUMBIAN GROUND SQUIRREL